DISCARD

Contemporary African Americans

WYNTON MARSALIS

BY
VERONICA FREEMAN ELLIS

RSVP

**RAINTREE
STECK-VAUGHN**
P U B L I S H E R S
The Steck-Vaughn Company

Austin, Texas

Published by Raintree Steck-Vaughn, an imprint of Steck-Vaughn Company.
Produced by Mega-Books, Inc.
Design and Art Direction by Michaelis/Carpelis Design Associates.
Cover photo: ©Abramson/Gamma-Liaison

Library of Congress Cataloging-in-Publication Data
Ellis, Veronica Freeman.
    Wynton Marsalis / by Veronica Freeman Ellis.
        p. cm. — (Contemporary African Americans)
    Includes bibliographical references (p. 47) and index.
    Summary: Discusses the personal life and musical career of the African-American trumpet player known for his performances of popular jazz and classical music.
    ISBN 0-8172-3988-X (Hardcover)
    ISBN 0-8172-6877-4 (Softcover)
    1. Marsalis, Wynton, 1961—Juvenile literature.   2. Trumpet players—United States—Biography—Juvenile literature.   3. Jazz musicians—United States—Biography—Juvenile literature.   4. Afro-American musicians—Biography—Juvenile literature.
[1. Marsalis, Wynton, 1961–   .   2. Trumpet players.   3. Afro-Americans—Biography.]
I. Title. II. Series.
ML3930.M327E45   1997
788.9'2' 092—dc21   96-47440
[B]   CIP
                                                                      AC MN
Printed and bound in the United States.

1 2 3 4 5 6 7 8 9 LB 00 99 98 97 96

Photo credits: ©John Spellman/Retna Ltd.: p.4; ©Stephanie Berger/Archives of Lincoln Center for the Performing Arts, Inc.: p. 7; AP/Wide World Photos, Inc.: pp. 8, 16, 29, 33, 34, 36; ©Frank Stewart: p.12; ©Enid Farber/Retna Ltd.: pp. 15, 26; ©Stephen Gates/People Weekly: p. 19; ©Leon Morris/Redfems/Retna Ltd.: p. 20; Archive Photos/Metronome Collection: p. 22; ©David Redfern/Retna Ltd.: pp. 25, 43; ©J. McNally/Sygma: p. 30; ©Sony Music/Frank Stewart: p. 39; ©C. Johnson/Gamma Liaison: p. 40.

Contents

ARTISTIC DIRECTOR

Wynton Marsalis stands before a group of young people in a concert hall at Lincoln Center for the Performing Arts, in New York City. He is explaining rhythm, one of the basics of music. To help his audience understand what rhythm is, he uses an everyday example.

Wynton asks them to think about the sounds they hear in the city—the traffic, the people talking, and the noise. In the midst of the noise, someone blows his car horn in a rhythmic pattern: "duh, duh ta duh." Wynton points out that the motorist blows his horn in a definite rhythm that makes you smile and think, "I know just how you feel." When you hear one motorist create a rhythm, Wynton says, "it makes

It is very important to Wynton Marsalis to pass along his knowledge of music and his love of jazz to young people.

you feel good because you realize that it's music."

Making people feel good through music is what Wynton Marsalis's life is about. He is one of the best and most popular jazz musicians alive today. He is also a leading classical trumpet player.

As Artistic Director of Jazz at Lincoln Center, Wynton promotes jazz and encourages an appreciation of all music. In this position he performs in concerts, plans film presentations, gives lectures, and participates in national tours. He also composes a new musical work each year for the program. These are tremendous and important tasks, but he carries out each one with confidence and skill. And he works to add to the vision of Lincoln Center, which, since the 1960s, has been to share the best of the performing arts with the public.

Lincoln Center is an ideal location for such a program. The Center is also home to many of New York City's leading performing arts groups, including the New York Philharmonic, the New York City Ballet, and the Metropolitan Opera. The Juilliard School—one of the best schools for performing arts in the world—is also located there.

Jazz at Lincoln Center was born in 1987, when Wynton developed a special concert and lecture series as part of the Center's existing Classical Jazz program. Now a permanent part of Lincoln Center, Jazz at Lincoln Center has grown to include films and educational programs, as well as concerts and lectures. It has brought the swinging, soulful style of

Lincoln Center for the Performing Arts is a group of buildings on the Upper West Side of New York City. It is home to theaters of dance, opera, music, and film, as well as to two schools and the music branch of the New York Public Library.

traditional jazz to the Center's jazz offerings and made them even more interesting and exciting.

The Lincoln Center Jazz Orchestra is an important part of the Jazz at Lincoln Center activities. Led by Wynton, it performs at the Center and on national tours. It also participates in the Jazz for Young People programs at the Center.

The Center's orchestra is a perfect showcase for the talent, inspiration, and hard work of the jazz musicians who perform there. Wynton wants everyone, especially young people, to understand and enjoy jazz because it is a musical form that is at the very heart of American culture.

Wynton pours his talent and inspiration into his

Wynton Marsalis attends an exhibit of children's art where he received an award from the Guggenheim Museum in New York City.

work with young people. He gives special concerts for young audiences. He opens the door to an art form that most people think only adults can appreciate and understand. Wynton believes he is able to explain jazz to young people because so many great jazz musicians spent time with him during his youth. He wants to help young people grow musically as others have helped him.

Chapter

A YOUNG TRUMPETER

The second of six boys (Branford, Wynton, Delfeayo, Ellis III, Mboya, and Jason), Wynton entered a world of music when he was born to Dolores and Ellis Marsalis on October 18, 1961, in New Orleans, Louisiana.

Wynton's father, Ellis, gave Wynton his start on the trumpet at age six. At the time, Ellis was playing jazz piano in the band of the famous trumpeter Al Hirt. His older brother, Branford, was already playing the piano and the clarinet. His father didn't want Wynton to feel left out, so he asked Hirt for a loan to buy a trumpet. Instead of lending Ellis money, Hirt gave Wynton one of his trumpets.

Wynton says that his father inspired him to become a jazz musician. There was nothing else in his life—not in his surroundings, in his friends, in school, or on the radio—that pointed him in that direction. But he didn't start out playing jazz. It would take years for Wynton to find his way to that style of music.

Wynton had his first trumpet lesson when he was six. At the age of seven, he made his first public appearance and got a standing ovation for playing *The Marine Hymn* at a recital. But music hadn't become important to him yet. His second trumpet lesson came when he was about ten. Then the next one was at age 12. He said he always asked his teachers how he could get better without practicing. If they couldn't tell him, he wouldn't go back for another lesson with them.

At age 12 his attitude changed. "I looked around and wanted to find something that I could do," he said. "I thought I would play basketball, but I wasn't good enough. . . . So I got into the band, and I couldn't play. . . .I was one of those [guys] that wanted to act like they could play without practicing."

That same year Wynton started taking lessons from John Longo, who was trained in both classical music and jazz. Longo, Wynton said, made him want to go home and practice.

Wynton began shedding, a jazz word he picked up from his father that means practicing. The need for shedding became even clearer to Wynton when he and Branford auditioned for their high school band.

Wynton and Branford were attending the New Orleans Center for the Creative Arts (NOCCA), a public arts high school. Their father Ellis was a teacher at the school and was well known as a jazz pianist. The school's band instructor, George Marks,

Wynton blowing a toy trumpet and his older brother, Branford, playing a toy saxophone. The two boys would grow up to play these same instruments.

was delighted that Ellis Marsalis's sons wanted to join the band. But after hearing Wynton play during the audition, Mr. Marks asked, "Are you sure you're Ellis's son?"

Wynton soon began practicing more often. He said, "That's all I did—practice trumpet. I would wake up in the morning and start practicing. I'd go to school and think about practicing in the daytime. I would play band in the evening and come home and pull records and books out and practice."

Throughout his childhood and adolescence, Wynton had a very close relationship with his brother Branford. The brothers often performed duets, with Branford on clarinet and Wynton on trumpet.

In high school Wynton and Branford were part of a funk band called The Creators. Funk is a mixture of jazz, rock-and-roll, and rhythm and blues. The Creators were very popular and played at weddings, dances, proms, band competitions, and talent shows. It was a fantastic time in the brothers' lives.

Wynton feels that his closeness with his brother resulted from a perfect balance of their personalities. Wynton was the "hot and fiery" one—always ready to speak his mind and use harsh words; Branford was the "cool and diplomatic" one—always telling his younger brother to keep quiet, to slow down, and to think before speaking.

Wynton hopes that his own sons will be as close as he and his brother Branford have always been.

Branford and Wynton were so close growing up that Wynton admits that the loneliest year of his life was when Branford left home for college. The brothers had shared a room until that time, and Wynton was used to having Branford around. Wynton remembers that Branford had to have music playing in order to fall asleep; Wynton couldn't sleep with the music on, so he waited for his brother to fall asleep before turning off the music. Being the last to fall asleep never bothered Wynton, because he didn't (and still doesn't) like having to sleep. He can't help thinking that he's missing something when he sleeps.

It's just as well that Wynton became used to very little sleep, for his art requires many hours on the road, hours of practice, and hours onstage. Preparation for his demanding career began during his teenage years in Kenner, Louisiana, when he and Branford played many **gigs**. They got used to late nights, sometimes getting home after midnight. While reheating the dinner that their mother had left for them, the brothers would talk about their gig. Sometimes their voices were so loud that their mother had to remind them not to wake their brothers (Delfeayo, now a music producer and trombone player; Ellis III, presently in the computer business; Mboya, who lives at home; and Jason, who now plays the drums).

Despite the late hours that Wynton kept while playing with The Creators, he played first trumpet with the New Orleans Civic Orchestra and the Brass Quintet and had a straight-A average in school. His mother became a little concerned. "My poor little baby [was] working with all those older musicians. I was proud but worried that he might be too busy to enjoy adolescence," she said.

In high school Wynton started listening to the jazz tenor saxophonist John Coltrane and became more interested in jazz. He said that the thing that attracted him to this music was that it was hard. Wynton knew he couldn't just sit down and play it. He said that when he played funk with The Creators, they would learn a tune in half an hour. "Jazz," Wynton says, "is eighty times harder."

While he was growing up, most of Wynton's experience with jazz came from listening to records and also to his father's bands. The closest he came to performing jazz was working with The Creators. Performing classical music was his first interest. He even used most of the money he earned by playing with The Creators to buy the different types of trumpets he needed in order to play classical baroque music.

Classical music was where Wynton first made his mark. When Wynton went to New York City to audition for the Tanglewood Music Center's summer program in 1978, he impressed the judges with his playing of a Haydn trumpet concerto. He then offered to play Bach's extremely difficult

Branford and Wynton Marsalis have performed together since they were in high school and even had a funk band called The Creators.

Second Brandenburg Concerto. While Wynton was warming up behind a pillar, Tanglewood's Artistic Director, Gunther Schuller, spied him talking to his trumpet, saying, "Now don't let me down." Schuller says he and the other judges were overwhelmed by his talent, and Wynton spent that summer at Tanglewood.

Wynton graduated high school in 1979 and received scholarship offers from Yale and other respected universities. Instead he chose to accept a scholarship from the Juilliard School, in New York City, and continue his study of music.

In 1980, while still a student at Juilliard, Wynton joined drummer Art Blakey's band, The Jazz Messengers, and in 1981 he toured Japan with

Pianist and producer Herbie Hancock is one of the great jazz musicians with whom Wynton Marsalis has played.

pianist Herbie Hancock. These experiences, as well as the support of his musical family, helped Wynton to grow into an outstanding jazz musician who is worthy of New Orleans's great jazz heritage.

Chapter *Three*

THE GREAT
JAZZ HERITAGE

New Orleans is considered the birthplace of jazz. It is also home to many cultures whose origins can be traced to West Africa, Europe, and Latin America. Jazz contains traces of rhythms and musical patterns from each of these groups. It is a unique art form that is the perfect expression of American culture. Jazz greats such as Louis "Satchmo" Armstrong and Duke Ellington, as well as other legendary jazz artists, expressed that culture through the music they played.

Today Wynton stresses the importance of jazz's history and development in understanding this music. But he had shown little interest in New Orleans's jazz heritage while growing up. He had never heard any of the older jazz musicians who played traditional Dixieland-style jazz at New Orleans's Preservation Hall. As a teenager he had learned about jazz from listening to records and reading books and from his father, Ellis.

His father was the first to set an example for Wynton of how to be a good musician. In addition to showing him how important it is to practice, Ellis also taught Wynton how to behave with audience members who go backstage after performances to ask for autographs. From years of watching his father's interaction with people, Wynton learned to treat fans with friendliness, respect, and patience.

Ellis also taught other aspiring young musicians besides his sons. While a teacher at the New Orleans Center for the Creative Arts, his students included his sons Branford, Wynton, and Delfeayo. Other former students are trumpeter Terence Blanchard, pianist and vocalist Harry Connick, Jr., trumpeter Donald Harrison, flutist Kent Jordan, trumpeter Marlon Jordan, and trumpeter Nicholas Payton. All of these young men are now famous jazz musicians.

In 1986 Ellis was invited to become the coordinator of Jazz Studies at Virginia Common- wealth University in Richmond. He accepted the invitation but in 1989 decided to return to New Orleans to head the Jazz Studies Program at the University of New Orleans. Ellis still holds this position, teaching and nurturing more young musicians just as he taught and nurtured his sons.

When Wynton went to New York City and joined Art Blakey's Jazz Messengers, he got a chance to play with a man who was not just a great jazz musician. Art Blakey was also a great jazz teacher. For over 40 years, Blakey made the Jazz Messengers a training ground for up-and-coming jazz musicians. Blakey taught these musicians—including Wynton—how to play as a band, how to dress and act onstage, and how to be leaders of their own bands. This passing on of knowledge is a jazz tradition that Wynton would later take responsibility for in his own bands.

While in the Jazz Messengers, Wynton met two more people who would further his jazz education—writer and jazz critic Stanley Crouch and writer Albert Murray. Crouch was amazed at how little young Wynton knew about jazz history. So Crouch took him under his wing. He introduced him to the music of Ornette Coleman, Duke Ellington, Thelonious

Ellis Marsalis (left) has taught many young jazz musicians throughout his career. Here he is pictured with sons Branford (center) and Delfeayo.

Monk, and other jazz greats who would have a deep effect on Wynton's later work. Crouch loaned Wynton records and books, took him to jazz clubs, and talked with him about jazz. He also introduced him to Albert Murray, who wrote, among other works, *Stomping the Blues*, an important book about African-American music.

Murray took Wynton to bookstores and museums and got him reading philosophy and great literature, as well as books on music. A great admirer of Duke Ellington, Murray taught Wynton about Ellington's

Ellis Marsalis is also a noted jazz pianist. Here he performs at the New Orleans Jazz Festival with Wynton on trumpet.

life and the music Ellington composed and conducted.

Wynton's father had tried before to get Wynton to listen to New Orleans jazz trumpeter Louis Armstrong. But it was Crouch who helped Wynton understand Armstrong's importance. Armstrong was the first to use organized solos in his performances. Organized solos are prearranged solos given by each member of a jazz group to showcase his or her talent.

Another early jazz musician whom Wynton came to appreciate is pianist Jelly Roll Morton. Wynton calls Morton "jazz's first intellectual." Morton developed a form of notation that makes it possible to write down jazz music and still keep its inventive **improvisational** quality that makes jazz what it is.

Studying Jelly Roll Morton's works also helped Wynton to better understand pianist and composer Duke Ellington. Wynton says that Ellington was the "greatest intellectual of jazz" because he wrote down and arranged the music. "He put it down, like Bach did for European music." Listening to Ellington, Wynton's favorite composer, and studying his works have greatly affected Wynton's own abilities to compose music and to create new interpretations of jazz classics.

There are many other talented jazz artists who have influenced Wynton. From saxophonist Charlie Parker, Wynton learned more about the organization within a piece of music. He also appreciates Parker's soulful blues sound. Wynton identifies saxophonist

The musician and composer whom Wynton Marsalis admires most is Edward Kennedy "Duke" Ellington.

John Coltrane as an example for all musicians because Coltrane's development came from very hard work. The trumpet players Dizzy Gillespie and Miles Davis were very important influences on Wynton's own playing style.

Wynton takes each earlier musician's unique jazz style into consideration as he perfects his craft. These great artists' contributions have shaped Wynton's approach to his art and made him an even better jazz musician and composer.

JAZZ MUSICIAN, JAZZ COMPOSER

In 1980, at age 19 and still a Juilliard student, Wynton signed his first recording contract with Columbia Records. Pianist Herbie Hancock produced the young trumpeter's debut album, *Wynton Marsalis*, which was nominated for a Grammy Award. Since then Wynton's recording career has soared, with his albums quickly rising to the top of the jazz charts.

In 1981 Wynton left Blakey's Jazz Messengers to form his own band. Along with his father and Branford, he is featured on the 1981 Columbia recording, *Fathers and Sons*. In 1982 Branford joined Wynton's band. The following year, Wynton's second album—and first album with his band—*Think of One* was released. This album went on to win a Grammy.

Wynton has recorded over 32 albums, several of which have been produced by his younger brother Delfeayo. Among Wynton's many jazz recordings are *Crescent City Christmas*; *Hot House Flowers*; *In This*

23

House, On This Morning; Marsalis Standard Time; Soul Gesture Vol. 1: Thick in the South; Soul Gesture Vol. 2: Uptown Ruler; The London Concert; Joe Cool's Blues; and *Citi Movement.*

In 1985 Branford left Wynton's band to play with the pop artist Sting. Wynton had to regroup and in 1987 formed the Wynton Marsalis Septet. When Wynton put his band together, he knew that the entire jazz world would be watching. He recruited the finest musicians for his seven-member band, some of whom had studied with his father. The band at first consisted of pianist Marcus Roberts, trombonist Wycliffe Gordon, bassist Reginald Veal, tenor saxophonist Todd Williams, alto saxophonist Wess Anderson, and drummer Herlin Riley. Later the makeup of the Septet changed to include pianist Eric Reed, saxophonist Victor Goines, and bassist Ben Wolfe. Wynton's band toured the United States and the world.

Being on the road with his band was a wonderful experience for Wynton. The Septet toured the United States by bus. The band played outdoor jazz festivals, including the Newport Jazz Festival. This festival is held every summer in Newport, Rhode Island, and was one of the first series of concerts in the United States to be devoted entirely to jazz.

The Septet also played at many indoor concerts around the country. The Septet had a special treat for their audiences at the end of many performances. For an **encore** the band members would begin a New

Wynton and his Septet have toured the United States playing at concerts and outdoor jazz festivals.

Orleans-style march out of the concert hall into the street. Still enjoying the music, the happy audience would follow the procession.

Touring with the band also gave Wynton the chance to meet many different kinds of people after performances. Countless audience members have left Wynton's dressing room remembering his friendly smile, his close and patient attention to what they say, and his sincere answers to their questions.

Wynton is especially fond of young people. One of his favorite things to do is to invite them to play his trumpet, the Monette Raja. Wynton's trumpet has an unusual built-in mouthpiece and was made by Dave Monette, who says his cat gave him the idea for the

25

trumpet's unique design. When young people visit Wynton backstage, he takes extra time to give advice to those who are up-and-coming musicians. In this way Wynton feels he can encourage them to continue their music education.

Wynton also spends time with young musicians because it reminds him of a special event that occurred when he was a teenager. At age 15 Wynton had a chance to meet the great trumpeter Clark Terry. On the morning after their first meeting, Terry got up early just to hear Wynton play Bach's *Second Brandenburg Concerto* with the New Orleans Symphony. Later, during one of Terry's tours, he sent Wynton a postcard from Europe. Terry's kindness and

Trumpeter Clark Terry performing with Wynton at the Village Vanguard, a jazz club in New York City.

interest encouraged the young trumpeter, and the experience has remained with Wynton ever since.

Remembering meetings such as the one with Terry is what motivates Wynton to stay backstage, no matter how tired he is, until he has signed the very last autograph and spoken to the last fan. Chats with audience members make Wynton feel as good backstage as when he is playing onstage with his band.

Wynton believes that making audiences feel good is the best part about being a jazz performer. He believes that the way jazz makes listeners feel is a result of the way musicians practice their art.

According to Wynton jazz has several basic traits, or special features. The reason for the spirited and positive emotions that jazz produces is because of its nonmusical traits and musical traits.

Some of the nonmusical traits are: (1) playing with a theme or an idea the way people can play with a ball; (2) having the desire to play with other people, which means letting others have a turn to play, just as in a game; (3) respecting individuality, which is the willingness to listen to other people's ideas and discuss those ideas.

Among the musical traits are: (1) playing in a way that brings out the emotions of the blues—disappointment, happiness, joy, sorrow—and the ability to play all of these emotions in one piece of music; (2) making the music swing, which means every beat must work together to hold the rhythm together;

(3) improvising, or the ability to make up music as a group; (4) challenging the rhythm (syncopation) and being prepared to do the unexpected; (5) using **call and response**; (6) playing the instruments in a way that makes them sing, shout, moan, growl, cry, or scream; (7) making use of the "spirit of worldliness" that is contained in jazz. This means making use of the connection that jazz has to music from other parts of the world, especially folk music and classical music.

After several successful years with the Septet, Wynton realized that touring with his band left little time for composing. So in December 1994, he dissolved the Septet. Since then Wynton has spent a great deal of time developing his artistic directorship of the Jazz at Lincoln Center program. This includes playing with the Lincoln Center Jazz Orchestra and composing new musical works for it.

Wynton's favorite duty as the Artistic Director is playing trumpet solos with the Lincoln Center Jazz Orchestra. *They Came to Swing*, the Orchestra's third album, features solos by Wynton on the track "Black and Tan Fantasy." *They Came to Swing* contains many Duke Ellington pieces, as well as works by other noted artists. A highlight of the album is one of Wynton's original compositions, "Express Crossing."

One of Wynton's most recent orchestral compositions is "Blood on the Fields," written as part of his Lincoln Center commitment to write a new work each year. The piece has met with tremendous success. Wynton

The Lincoln Center Jazz Orchestra, with Wynton conducting, in rehearsal for a tribute to jazz legend Louis Armstrong.

says "Blood on the Fields" has "the deepest blues," and it brought tears to his eyes when he wrote it.

The main inspiration for many of Wynton's compositions comes from his experiences growing up in New Orleans. Inspiration has also come from his band members. One composition in particular, "In This House, On This Morning," was inspired by Wynton and his former band members' experiences going to church when they were growing up. Some band members had sung or played a musical instrument as part of the church services.

Before he began composing "In This House, On

This Morning," Wynton decided to talk to other people about similar experiences. He talked to an African-American minister about the form of African-American church services. The minister explained how many services follow a call and response pattern. In music, call and response occurs when a singer or musician sings or plays part of a melody and another one responds, or answers back, with another part of the melody. It is like a conversation. In church, the call and response form of the service is "a dialogue with divinity, a conversation between people and God," said the minister. Wynton went on to use the call and response form in "In This House, On This

Many of Wynton Marsalis's jazz compositions have their roots in African-American sacred music.

Morning" to remind listeners of this conversation with God in church.

Wynton believes that jazz is also about "the dialogue, the quality of conversation." And it is exactly that dialogue that Wynton wants to bring out in his jazz compositions and performances. Yet his talent lies not in jazz alone but also in classical music, a fact that has enabled him to rise to the top in both musical worlds.

BRIDGING THE MUSIC WORLDS

Wynton's training in both jazz and classical music sets him apart as a musician. Many people feel that Wynton's classical performances are as superb as his jazz performances.

Wynton appreciates both classical music and jazz, but he prefers jazz. He believes jazz gives musicians the freedom to have their own vision. Classical performers, he says, can only interpret the vision of the composer. In other words, they have to play the music as the composer wrote it. In jazz, performers can improvise when they play. Improvising means making it up as you go along.

According to Wynton improvisation gives jazz musicians the freedom to be creative. But this doesn't mean jazz musicians can do whatever they want. Wynton compares a jazz band improvising to a basketball team playing basketball. He points out that even though a team might not know which play is

Wynton has won a number of Grammy Awards for his contributions to jazz and classical music.

next, the players—the guards, forwards, and center— each have a special job. So no matter what happens, the guards know their job is to guard the basketball. Each player in a jazz band has a special job, too. So when the trumpeter starts to improvise, for example, the bass player has to keep the rhythm going because that's his job. The combination of structure and freedom in jazz gives musicians the opportunity to put their personalities into their playing.

Despite the major differences between classical and jazz music, Wynton can perform within the limits of classical music and flourish in the freedom of jazz.

In 1983 he stunned everyone in the music business by being the first performer to win Grammy Awards for both jazz and classical recordings. The winning jazz recording was *Think of One*, and the winning classical recording was *Haydn: Trumpet Concerto in E-flat/Mozart: Trumpet Concerto in D/Hummel: Trumpet Concerto in E-flat.*

In 1984 he repeated the feat. The jazz winner was Wynton's *Hot House Flowers*, and the classical winner was *Wynton Marsalis—Edita Gruberová—Handel, Purcell, Torelli, Fasch, Molter.*

In recognition of his achievements and contributions

In 1995 Wynton Marsalis received honorary degrees from Yale University and, as photographed here, from the Manhattan School of Music.

to music, Wynton has been honored by a number of institutions. He has received honorary doctor of fine arts degrees from Manhattan College of Music in New York, and from Princeton University in New Jersey. Yale University in Connecticut, awarded him an honorary doctor of music degree. From New York's Hunter College, Wynton received an honorary doctor of letters degree. In June 1996 *Time* magazine named him one of the 25 most influential people in the United States.

These honors are important to Wynton because they serve as his musical bridge to different cultures. These honors not only connect the jazz and classical music worlds, but they also connect the worlds of international audiences. Wynton has won audiences all over the world with his inspired performances. He is particularly honored in Japan and is one of its most popular jazz artists. He has appeared as a soloist with many of the world's leading symphony orchestras. He has a strong following with both jazz and classical music fans in Europe.

Once, on a European tour stop in Marciac, France, Wynton and his band entertained guests at a party with a performance of the song "Stardust." The music was so moving, it made one of the women in the audience cry. During another tour stop in London, Wynton played the Haydn Trumpet Concerto in E-flat with the English Chamber Orchestra. The audience had a similar reaction to this beautiful piece of music.

Wynton has brought his music around the world. Here Spanish opera singer Placido Domingo performs with Wynton at the Concert for Planet Earth, in Rio de Janeiro, Brazil.

And in Chiba, Japan, he amazed the audience by playing a jam session—a spur of the moment improvisation session—with the famous jazz drummer Elvin Jones.

From classical music to jazz, Wynton has bridged the world. His workshops on music education and jazz have strengthened that bridge. He has helped individuals of all ages and ethnic groups to understand classical music and jazz. He has taken his message throughout the United States and around the world, for he is on a mission to keep all music alive in the hearts, minds, and souls of all people.

KEEPING JAZZ ALIVE

Wynton Marsalis's work has brought an increasingly larger audience to jazz. Through his efforts more and more people have come to understand the important place that jazz has in American culture and history.

In 1994 Wynton's book on jazz, *Sweet Swing Blues on the Road*, was published. Wynton thought a book about jazz bands was important because few people understand how difficult it is to travel 300 days out of the year.

Photographer Frank Stewart traveled around with Wynton and the Septet for a year and took pictures of them every chance he got. Wynton wrote about the kinds of people and places the band was able to visit. He tells of composing and performing with old-time jazz musicians in New Orleans one week and performing classical music in Europe the next. Wynton's words and Stewart's photographs are considered some of the best descriptions of jazz artists on the road ever published.

Despite his busy musical life, *Sweet Swing Blues on the Road* shows that Wynton still finds time to visit his parents and spend time with his children, Wynton and Simeon. Wynton guards the privacy of his children and their mother very closely. He does not talk about them in interviews, and they are almost never mentioned in articles about Wynton. In the book, however, Wynton gives us a brief glimpse of his sons. He describes how the boys play something they call "jazz blues." Little Wynton plays the drums or beats on anything handy. Simeon picks up anything that looks like a trumpet and pretends to play.

Sweet Swing Blues on the Road also captures Wynton's dedication to his job as a diplomat for music. Although he spends only 40 to 50 days out of the year at home in his New York City apartment, this spokesman for jazz takes every opportunity to visit schools. On these visits he spends a great deal of time explaining to young people about many different musical styles. His main goal is to make it easier for children to make music a part of their lives.

"No school is too bad for me to go to. . . . I'll try to teach anybody. We are all striving for the same thing, to make our community stronger and richer. That's what the jazz musician has always been about."

Another reason Wynton spends so much time traveling to schools is that he believes that jazz

Wynton always makes time to give talks and lectures to children. He feels that understanding basic musical ideas adds to the enjoyment of music.

teaches the basics of respect. For Wynton and many other musicians, jazz means learning to communicate with and respect each human being.

To help reach this goal, Wynton has put together Lincoln Center's Jazz for Young People concerts. He has also hosted a Public Broadcasting System (PBS) program, *Marsalis on Music*. The four-part series for young audiences was aired weekly, beginning in October 1995. In addition to Wynton and the Lincoln Center Jazz Orchestra, the program featured cellist Yo-Yo Ma, conductor Seiji Ozawa, who is the music director of the Boston Symphony Orchestra, and the Tanglewood Music Center Orchestra. The four parts that make up the program are "Why Toes Tap: Rhythm," "Listening for Clues: Form," "Sousa to Satchmo: The Wind Band and the Jazz Band," and "Tackling the Monster: Practice."

Wynton hoped these programs would bring children "into the magical world of music" and help them to understand some basic musical elements, such as rhythm and form. Through the program, he wanted to demonstrate how important it is to listen to different kinds of music. Once people begin to listen, Wynton believes they can discover how different forms

Music is one key to freedom of expression, and Wynton believes it is a form of communication that makes one's life better.

of music are related, even though they may seem quite different at first.

Wynton was especially pleased when *Marsalis on Music* was published as a book with a compact disc to go along with it. Many times it is just as important to read about jazz as it is to listen to it. Reading about jazz is another way to experience the history of it and to understand the reasons why jazz musicians do what they do. This can be true about any form of art.

Everywhere he travels Wynton tells people that jazz is not only about listening but also about talking to different kinds of people and hearing and seeing how they view the world. "Jazz means learning to respect the individual," says Wynton. He explains that many times a musician may practice with him and have a completely different opinion of how a piece should be played. "That is when we come together and have a conversation," he says.

Wynton describes how these conversations lead to a combination of different versions of the same melody. "It's what makes jazz exciting and interesting at the same time," he explains. "That's why jazz is a great thing for kids to learn. It teaches people to have a conversation, a dialogue, and still keep their own point of view."

This is another way in which Wynton believes jazz is part of a community. "In communities where two or three people take an interest in something, the whole community will be uplifted." Wynton sees this happen over and over as he travels around the world.

In a program that aired on National Public Radio (NPR), Wynton set out to help listeners understand that jazz is not a mystery or just for a select group of people. It is for everyone. The 26-part radio series, *Jazz from NPR: Wynton Marsalis Making the Music*, began on January 7, 1996. Through jam sessions and informal discussions with **vibraphonist** Lionel Hampton, drummer Elvin Jones, pianist Ahmad Jamal, jazz singer Abbey Lincoln, and others, Wynton was able to share the magic of jazz with the listeners. In addition to Wynton and his guests talking about the history of jazz, they often gave performances that showcased its exciting freedom.

Through improvisation jazz musicians have the freedom to express themselves and stamp their identities on the music they play. However, within that freedom is respect for each group member—a respect that allows time for each musician to be the center of attention. And this is the central theme of jazz that Wynton brings to audiences. He often says, "Our music is about democracy, about freedom of speech."

In other words jazz musicians must use what they know about playing jazz to help the people who listen to their music to open up and express themselves and their emotions. "Take your freedom, and use it to help other people get freedom."

Wynton Marsalis is a devoted and passionate spokesman for jazz and for music education. He

Wynton's life work is to use music to help people respect one another.

hopes that his work at Lincoln Center and his recordings, lectures, and performances will help keep jazz alive and thriving. For Wynton Marsalis jazz comes down to making people happy—not just about themselves but about other people and the world around them.

1961   Born in New Orleans, Louisiana, on October 18.

1967   Receives first trumpet from trumpeter Al Hirt.
       Has first lesson.

1973   Has third trumpet lesson. Begins practicing more.

1979   Enrolls in the Juilliard School of Music,
       in New York City.

1980   Joins Art Blakey's band, The Jazz Messengers. Signs
       first recording contract with Columbia Records
       for debut album, *Wynton Marsalis*.

1981   Tours Japan with Herbie Hancock. Featured on
       Columbia recording *Fathers and Sons*.

1983   Columbia Records releases his second album,
       Think of One. Wins Grammy Awards for both jazz
       and classical recordings.

1984   Wins Grammy Awards for both jazz and classical
       recordings a second time.

1987   Forms jazz band the Wynton Marsalis Septet.
       Founds Jazz at Lincoln Center program.

1991   Named Artistic Director of Jazz at Lincoln Center.

1994   Dissolves the Wynton Marsalis Septet.

1995   Hosts Public Broadcasting System (PBS) program,
       Marsalis on Music. W. W. Norton and Company
       publishes companion book.

1996   Hosts 26-part National Public Radio (NPR) series, *Jazz from NPR: Wynton Marsalis Making the Music.* Named one of 25 most influential people in the United States by *Time* magazine.

Glossary

call and response   Singing or playing one portion of a song or melody and later having others respond by singing or playing another portion.

encore   An additional performance in response to an audience's enthusiasm.

gig   An engagement or booking for musicians; a job.

improvisation   The act of inventing, composing, or reciting without preparation.

vibraphone   A musical instrument similar to a xylophone but with metal bars.

Blumenthal, Bob. "Marsalis's Class." *The Boston Globe.* January 5, 1996.

"Branford Marsalis—The Chronology." "COLUMBIA" Registered U. S. Patent & Trademark Office. Sony Music Entertainment, Inc. Microsoft Internet Explorer, January 1996.

"Ellis Marsalis." "COLUMBIA" Registered U. S. Patent & Trademark Office. Sony Music Entertainment, Inc. Microsoft Internet Explorer, January 1996.

Garland, Phyl. "Wynton Marsalis, Musical Genius Reaches Top at 21." *Ebony.* March 1983.

"Jazz Man." *The Members Magazine.* Boston: WGBH (Channel 2), January 1996.

"Lincoln Center Jazz Orchestra." "COLUMBIA" Registered U. S. Patent & Trademark Office. Sony Music Entertainment, Inc. Microsoft Internet Explorer, January 1996.

Marsalis, Wynton. *Marsalis on Music.* New York: W. W. Norton & Company, 1995.

Marsalis, Wynton, and Frank Stewart. *Sweet Swing Blues on the Road.* New York: W. W. Norton & Company, 1994.

Martin, Ralph G. *Lincoln Center for the Performing Arts.* Englewood Cliffs, N.J.: Prentice-Hall, Inc., 1971.

Norment, Lynn. "Wynton Marsalis." *Ebony.* July 1994.

Rich, Alan. *The Lincoln Center Story.* New York: American Heritage, 1984.

Sancton, Thomas. "Horns of Plenty." *Time*. October 22, 1990.

Santoro, Gene. "Young Man with a Horn." *The Nation*. March 1, 1993.

Scherman, Tony. "What Is Jazz?" American Heritage, October 1995.

Sidran, Ben. *Talking Jazz: An Oral History.* New York: Da Capo Press, Inc., 1992.

"The 25 Most Influential People in America." *Time*. June 17, 1996.

Watrous, Peter. "Wynton's Septet Sounds Its Last Notes." *San Francisco Chronicle*. December 2, 1994.

Wynn, Ron, ed. *All Music Guide to Jazz.* San Francisco: Miller Freeman Books, 1995.

"Wynton Marsalis—Facts." "COLUMBIA" Registered U. S. Patent & Trademark Office. Sony Music Entertainment, Inc. Microsoft Internet Explorer, January 1996.